£2.70

Printed and Published in Great Britain by D. C. THOMSON & CO., LTD.,
185 Fleet Street, London EC4A 2HS.
© D. C. THOMSON & CO., LTD., 1987.
ISBN 0 85116 401 3

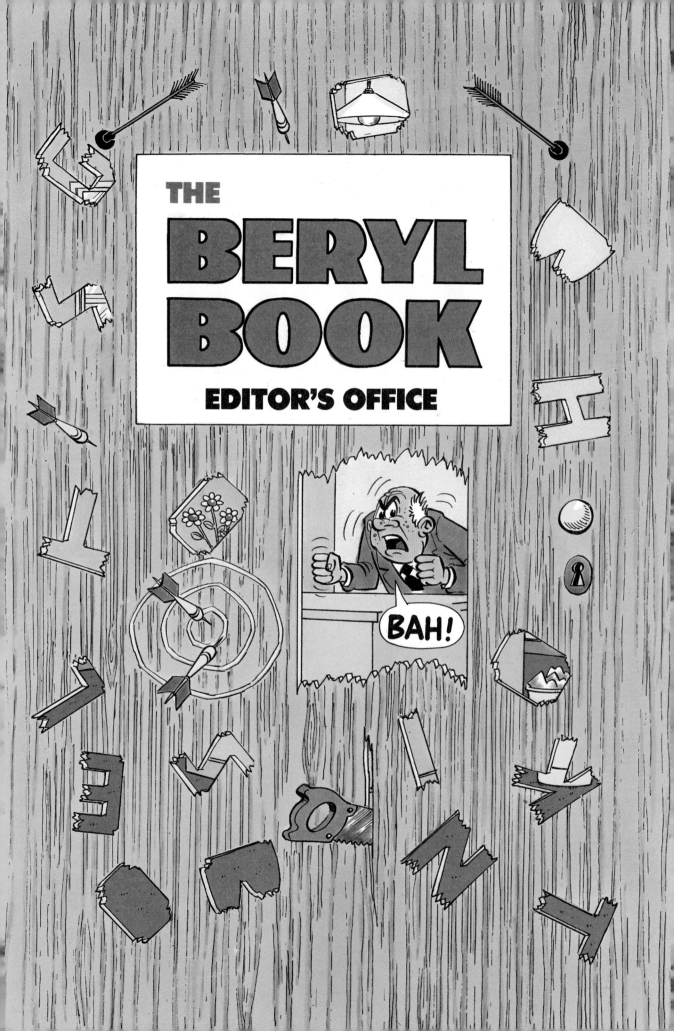

Along the page-tops, for you folks,
Look out for lots of perilous jokes!
Signed Beryl

WHAT A DUMMY!

DAD:— " I don't like all these flies buzzing round my food."
ME:— "Well, pick out the ones you like and I'll swat the others!"

AUNT:— "I'm going home tomorrow, Beryl. Are you sorry?"
ME:— "Yes, I thought it was today!"

PERILOUS PENALTY!

COWHAND CACKLES!

MUM:— "Why do you want the chair that Uncle Freddy's sitting on?"
ME:— "Because my ice cream cone is on it, too!"

COLLECTOR:— "Would you care to give anything for the dogs' home?"
ME:— "Certainly. Here's a ham-bone!"

DAD:— "Who gave you that black eye?"
ME:— "Nobody — I had to fight for it!"

DAD:— "I can't help with your homework. It wouldn't be right."
ME:— "Maybe not. But you couldn't be any worse than me!"

CYNTHIA:— "How did you find the weather when you were away?"
ME:— "I just went outside and there it was!"

TEACHER:- "If you take twenty from thirty, what's the difference?"
ME:- "That's what I say — who cares?"

Perilous hints on WOODWORK

CYNTHIA:- "What is the hide of a cow used for?"
ME:- "It keeps the cow together!"

GROCER:— "You say that banana I sold you is useless. Why?"
ME:— "Well, two people stood on the skin, and didn't fall!"

TEACHER:- "Who went into the lions' den and came out alive?" ME:- "Er . . . the lions?"

HOW AM I EXPECTED TO FLY, WHEN YOU BLOCK MY RUNWAY?

I'LL JUST HAVE TO KEEP TRYING.

YAHOO! WE HAVE LIFT-OFF!

BAH! FAILED AGAIN!

SHPLURT!

I'M NOT GONNA GIVE UP!

PHOOEY! YOU'LL NEVER FLY!

OH, YEAH? WELL, I BET YOU TEN PENCE EACH THAT I'LL BE FLYING BY THIS AFTERNOON!

YOU'RE ON! OUR MONEY COULDN'T BE SAFER!

THEN—

READY, BERYL? IT'S TIME TO GO.

OH, BOY! SUPER!

FOLLOW ME, THEN, YOU LOT, AN' YOU'LL SEE ME FLYING.

TEN MINUTES LATER . . .

GARGLE! WE SHOULD'VE KNOWN SHE'D DIDDLE US!

CHEAT! UNFAIR!

IT'S A FIDDLE!

WE'VE BEEN DONE!

HAR! HAR! YOU LOT DIDN'T KNOW ABOUT THIS! HAVE YOUR CASH READY WHEN WE LAND, SUCKERS! HO! HO! HO! HO!

PLEASURE FLIGHTS £250 PER PERSON

DOPEY DAVE:— "Why doesn't that bull have horns?"
ME:— "Well, mainly because it's a horse!"

TEACHER:— "What is the meaning of 'silence'?"
ME:— "It's what you don't hear when you listen."

TIP-TOPPER

BURGLAR TRAP!

DAD:— "Beryl will go a long way with her fiddle."
NEIGHBOUR:— "Good! When does she leave?"

CYNTHIA:— "Is Violet any good at the long jump?"
ME:— "Huh! She can hardly clear her throat!"

ME (lying in bed):— "Gosh! It's quarter past eight! If Mum doesn't wake me soon, I'll be late for school!"

TEACHER:— "Beryl, can you give me a proverb?"
ME:— "Yes, miss. A sock on the foot is worth two on the nose!"

MUM:— "How dare you call your Aunt stupid. Apologise at once."
ME:— "I'm sorry you're so stupid, Auntie!"

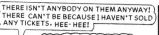

Dad:— "I don't know why you're grumbling! This is nice tea."
ME:— "I s'pose it is — but Mum says it's soup!"

GAMEKEEPER:- "Didn't you see the notice 'No Fishing Allowed'?"
ME:- "Sure, but I'm fishing quietly."

TEACHER:- "What do we make from horn?"
ME:- "Hornaments, sir!"

CYNTHIA:- "What has ten legs but can't walk?"
ME:- "Five pairs of trousers!"

Perilous hints on GARDENING

CYNTHIA:— "Have you ever been bitten by an ant?"
ME:— "No, but I've been spanked by an uncle!"

MUM:— "I'm surprised at finding you drinking all the lemonade."
ME:— "So am I! I thought you were out!"

ME:- "Sorry I'm late, sir — I sprained my ankle!"
TEACHER:- "Huh! Another lame excuse!"

INVISIBLE BANANAS!

TEACHER:— "What is nothing?"
ME:— "Er . . . a footless stocking without a leg!"

CLOSE ENCOUNTERS OF THE PERILOUS KIND
WOW! A REAL FLYING SAUCER LANDING IN OUR GARDEN! MUST SEE IF THERE ARE ANY SPACE-MEN IN IT!

CYNTHIA:— "Can you stand on your head?"
ME:— "No, it's too high up!"

TEACHER:— "How many times have I told you to be here on time?"
ME:- "I don't know, sir. I thought YOU were keeping count!"

DAD:— "Did you get my boots soled?"
ME:— "Yes! I got two pounds for them!"

TEACHER:— "Now, Beryl, tell us what you know about the Iron Age."
ME:— "Er — I'm afraid I'm a bit rusty on that subject, sir!"

HELP LESS WITH LAUGHTER!

MUM:— "I wish your Dad would stay at home some evenings to see how you behave when he's out!"

DAD:— "What was that noise I heard in your room last night?"
ME:— "That was me falling asleep!"

TEACHER:— "How many p's in soup?"
ME:— "Oh . . . about half a pound!"

Bloke: — "Can you tell me the quickest way to the station?"
ME: — "Yes, jet-propelled roller-skates!"

DAD:— "Did they have a big gate at the football match?"
ME:— "Yes — biggest I've ever climbed!"

DAD-DIDDLING DISASTER!

MUM:— "What did I say I'd do to you if I caught you eating my cake?"
ME:— "That's funny, Mum. I've forgotten, too!"

COUSIN WILF:— "I've got a wonderful family tree."
ME:— "You'll be the sap, I suppose?"

DAD:-"Who broke this window?"
ME:-"Alfie. He ducked when I threw a ball at him!"

IF I WUZ DAD!

SMART ALEC:- "Our teacher talks to himself!"
ME:- "So does ours — but he thinks we're listening!"

AUNT:— "What do you do at school, Beryl?"
ME:— "I wait until it's time to come home again!"

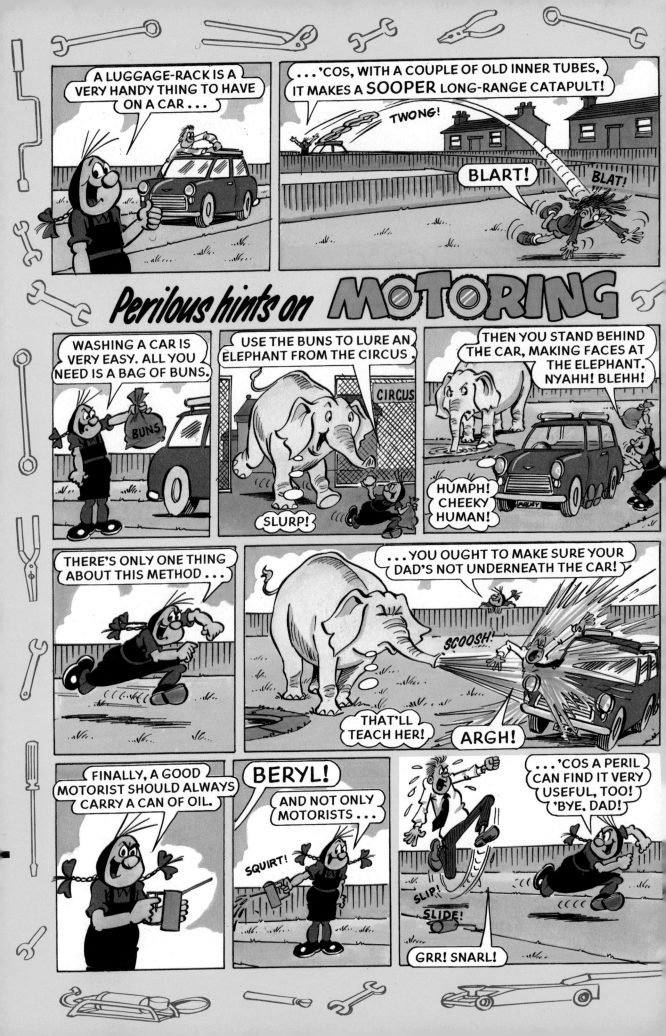

CYNTHIA:- "Ha! You're afraid to go upstairs by yourself in the dark!"
ME:- "No, I'm not! Just you come up with me and see!"

Cynthia: — "When is it bad luck to have a black cat cross your path?"
ME: — "When you're a mouse!"

ME:— "Tell me a true story."
DAD:— "Okay! I'll tell you about the time I was eaten by cannibals!"

CONDUCTOR:- "Gosh! A bloke's just fallen from the bus!"
ME:- "Don't worry! He's paid his fare!"

PERILOUS INVENTIONS

(ONE THAT BERYL WOULD MAKE RIGHT NOW — *IF SHE GOT THE CHANCE!*)

4. THE PAINLESS SLIPPER!

CYNTHIA:- "How do you make a sausage roll?"
ME:- "Put it on a hill and give it a shove!"

DAD:— "I know all there is to know about football."
ME:— "Is that so? Well, how many holes are there in a goal net?"